IN GOOD Company

The Pilgrim Press
Cleveland, Ohio

The Pilgrim Press
Cleveland, Ohio 44115

© 1998 by The Pilgrim Press

All rights reserved. Published 1998

Printed in Hong Kong
on acid-free paper

First printing

Welcome to another year of **In Good Company: A Woman's Journal for Spiritual Reflection.** This journal for 1999 continues the tradition of offering illuminating quotes from women and powerful images from some of today's most creative photographers, to refresh your soul and enrich your spiritual journey.

Special thanks to Curt Ackley, Kelley Baker, Blanche M. Brooks, Ed Huddleston, Audrey Miller, Mary Ann Murray, Katherine Negermajian, and Arlene Nehring for submitting quotes, and to Nancy Tenney for giving a careful eye to the work in progress; to Joan D. Chittister for her stirring introduction; to Martha Clark for her artistic genius; and to all the women and friends of women who find **In Good Company** a helpful journaling companion and share it with others.

May your days in good company with the women on these pages provide you with grace-filled insight, new vision, and a richness that will sustain you throughout the year.

LYNNE M. DEMING AND KATHLEEN C. ACKLEY

EDITORS

Introduction

People often say that [they] have not yet found themselves," the psychiatrist Thomas Szasz wrote in The
Second Sin. "But the self is not something one finds;
it is something one creates." What we too often misun-
derstand, perhaps, is that if we ever want to be whole, create a
self we must. But if truth were known, it is perfectly obvious that
there is a self inside each one of us that is forever trying to get
out. Wanting to become. Waiting to be found. Fearing to be lost.
Hoping to grow.　❧　There is a self in the subterranean center of a woman's soul that no one sees. We guard it jealousy, hide
it carefully, deny it mightily—and far, far too often—ignore it
successfully. We hide it sometimes even from ourselves. But hiding
what we are, even from ourselves, is a dangerous thing. It is precisely the denied parts of us, the hurting parts of us, the hoping
parts of us, that we must mine and polish and honor ourselves if
we are ever to have the truth of our lives honored by others.
❧　　It is the real self that a woman's spiritual journal is
designed to release.　❧　A personal journal is a mirror held
up to the part of us that hides for fear of being rejected by a
world that does not know us and, painful as it is to admit, does
not even care to know us. Journaling enables us to find the parts

of us that run from conflict, and love risk, and worry about fail-ure, and strive to achieve. In a journal we see them all at once and in all their conflicts. Journaling flushes out the self that is in camouflage and points out the self that is lacking. Journaling enables us to trace the inner map that leads to that part of the self that is yet a work in progress. ❧ *A spiritual journal opens us to ourselves and invites us to consider what we hesitate to admit, even to ourselves, what we exaggerate to everyone else, what we minimize to those around us. It exposes us to the sun-light of good sense, proper proportion, and radical honesty so that heartened by truth and prodded by authenticity we can marshal the strength to be who we really are now and gather the resolve to be who we most deeply want to be in the future. Whatever the cost. Once we begin as women to tell the truth about ourselves to ourselves we can tell it unceasingly to others. For their sakes as well as our own.* ❧ *"Those who swallow a stone become a stone," the proverb teaches. But what we do not allow to hide inside of us, like a dinosaur in a dungeon, cannot hurt us any-more. We learn to take the measure of its punyness. We pull its thorns from our hearts. We leap its limits. We exhaust the rage of it that smolders within us silently, despite our strict controls. And slowly, steadily, we reduce to size the hurts and stings, the fan-tasies and fears we expose to the scrutiny of every ripening dawn.* ❧ *We find inside ourselves, too, the aspirations and insights, the questions and concerns that are of our own making. We put down the expectations of others, the definitions of those who have defined us for their own sakes, the measuring sticks of people we've never met but by whose rules we have come to live. In a woman's spiritual journal, we wind our way through the ideas of our own that need to be pursued, that ought to be explored, that press to be replaced with newer, richer things to think about than what we have received prepackaged from the world around us but which are forever repressed, diminished, or denied for want of the courage to give them their due.* 🐚 *We come to realize that our own best thoughts are the site of God within the human heart to which we seldom listen. Journaling calls us to live the interior life with the same kind of care and intensity with which we live a public one.* 🐚 *Daily journals often intimidate us by virtue of their dailiness alone. Because we get too busy to journal, too tired to journal, too bored by our own repetitions, we stop. At least I do. Regularly. But then I remember that a spiritual journal is not necessarily a diary. It is a collection of moments that count for more than the day on which they occur. They are the moments to which we return on other days, at other times, to get our bearings, to measure our spiritual increase from one situation to the next, to test the level of the acids in our soul. No, dailiness is not the criterion for journal keeping. It is honesty and depth and impact that count. Then the days left blank from month to month can be used out of sequence to trace the ideas that appear over time, to assess their development, to calculate their meaning for our spiritual selves.* 🐚 *It is these moments, quietly kept,*

*gently revisited from time to trying time, that reveal us to our-
selves, that create the self of gold we are shaping within, that
uncage the bird of hope in us and let it free.* ❧ *A personal
journal is an autobiography of spiritual development. It invites
us to respond to the ideas of others. It enables a record of our
own. It provides a history of thought by which we can chart the
internal mountains we have already climbed as well as identify
those yet to come. It calls us to be honest with ourselves, a collo-
quy without which we can be honorable to no one else. Here in
the center of the self we can only be exactly who and what we
are. Here we give flesh and heart to the woman we want to
become.* ❧ *Setting out to tell ourselves the woman's truth
of our woman's life is a journey more circuitous than any walk in
the woods at midnight, more mysterious than any mystical cloud
of unknowing, more spiritually worthwhile than any penance we
can contemplate, more rewarding than any holy vision. Why?
Because the journaling process is the journey to the center of the
self where God resides in wait for us to complete the creation
which Goodness has begun.* ❧ *The self is not a prefabri-
cated edition of someone else. It is God and me in search of me
and all my fullness.*

JOAN D. CHITTISTER

Monday, December 28

*Women's prayers celebrate the
seasons of women's lives.*
—KAREN L. ROLLER

Tuesday, December 30

*There are only so many hours
in the day, and no one can be in
two places at once.*
—MARY CATHERINE BATESON

Wednesday, December 30

To survive and evolve as free
women, we must maintain unity
and draw on our inner resources.
—CHARLENE SPRETNAK

Thursday, December 31

NEW YEAR'S EVE

Acknowledging, owning, and
valuing the past . . . allows us to
begin to re-member and to feel safe
re-imagining the future.
—NANCY J. BERNEKING

Friday, January 1

NEW YEAR'S DAY

Through the days to come, in every
time of year or climate, may you
know the luminous goodness of
God, creator of all things, all people.

—JUDY NEWTON

Saturday, January 2

No one knows what lies ahead
when we say yes to God.

—JAN L. RICHARDSON

Sunday, January 5

JEREMIAH 31:7–14 OR SIRACH 24:1–12

PSALM 147:12–20 OR WISDOM OF SOLOMON 10:15–21

EPHESIANS 1:3–14

JOHN 1:(1–9), 10–18

In the beginning was the Word,

and the Word was with God,

and the Word was God.

—JOHN 1:1

*As I sit to write this morning, I **breathe** in and **breathe** out. . . . I **breathe** in, grateful for life, for my life, for the gift of it all. I **breathe** out, **yielding** my cares to the Mercy.*

—ELAINE M. PREVALLET

Monday, January 4

When we perceive ourselves as powerful, when we believe in that power, we appropriate the power within us.

—BARBARA STARRETT

Tuesday, January 5

Spirituality is expressed in everything we do.

—ANNE E. CARR

Wednesday, January 6

EPIPHANY

Walk in the light, and carry that
light to chase away the shadows in
which so many dwell.

—LAVON BAYLER

Thursday, January 7

May we discover that cooperation is
more fruitful than competition.

—EVELYN S. MURRAY

Friday, January 8

Teach us to listen to the stirring of
our own longings for there we will
discover You again.

—SHARON THORNTON

Saturday, January 9

Our prayerful listening to God
softens the hard and busy paths
that still crisscross our heart.

—WENDY MILLER

Sunday, January 10

ISAIAH 42:1-9

PSALM 29

ACTS 10:34-43

MATTHEW 3:13-17

*Ascribe to God the glory of God's
name; worship God in holy array.*

—PSALM 29:2

Until the **reconciliation** *of* **women** *and* **men** *as full facets of the* **face** *of God is complete, how can we possibly speak a reconciling word to the churches and the nations?*

—JOAN D. CHITTISTER

Monday, January 11

*If there is deep love involved, there
is deep responsibility toward it.*

—MAY SARTON

Tuesday, January 12

*God has made everything that is
made, and God loves everything
that [God] has made.*

—JULIAN OF NORWICH

Wednesday, January 13

When has someone's honest and
caring listening enabled you to
express and transform your anger?
—JAN L. RICHARDSON

Thursday, January 14

It is through our human experience
that we meet God.
—ELAINE M. WARD

Friday, January 15

As pieces of fabric, weave us
together in new patterns.
—UNITED CHURCH OF
CHRIST WOMEN

Saturday, January 16

The image of God as Mother of
the whole creation . . . is an image
of inclusive love.
—JUDITH PLASKOW AND
CAROL P. CHRIST

Sunday, January 17

ISAIAH **49:1–7**

PSALM **40:1–11**

1 CORINTHIANS **1:1–9**

JOHN **1:29–42**

God called me from the womb,

and from the body of my mother

God named my name.

—ISAIAH 49:1

*We all have bits and scraps of experience, dream, and thought out of which we **weave** the **texture,** the story, of our lives. The metaphors within which we reside **link us** to the symbolic quality of the divine.*

—LYNDA SEXSON

Monday, January 18

Womanist theology . . . must teach the church the different ways God reveals prophetic word and action for Christian living.

—DELORES S. WILLIAMS

Tuesday, January 19

If every day is an awakening, you will never grow old. You will just keep growing.

—GAIL SHEEHY

Wednesday, January 20

*The more you pray the more you
will be enlightened.*

—ANGELA OF FOLIGNO

Thursday, January 21

*Those who guide us up, over,
and around the boulders and
chasms of our lives reveal the
many faces of God.*

—JEAN M. BLOMQUIST

Friday, January 22

Spiritual journal writing can . . .
be a way of discovering what we
truly believe.

—ELAINE M. WARD

Saturday, January 23

Between invocation and
benediction is the possibility
of speaking justice.

—MAREN C. TIRABASSI

Sunday, January 24

*The people who sat without light
have seen a great light, and for
those who sat in the region and
shadow of death light has dawned.*

—MATTHEW 4:16

*Unless we are able to realize the **grace of God** as it comes to us through friendship, **pets,** and nature, through **prayer** and **solitude,** through solidarity with others in suffering and struggle, through lovemaking, music, play, and meaningful work, we are likely to burn out, give up, or go mad.*

— CARTER HEYWARD

Monday, January 25

Tuesday, January 26

Wednesday, January 27

*To imagine the Divine Feminine is
to meet a deeply felt need. It is also
to turn our priorities topsy-turvy.*

—CONNIE ZWEIG

Thursday, January 28

*To exercise our transformative
power, we must be able
to bond together.*

—JANET KALVEN AND

MARY I. BUCKLEY

Friday, January 29

_All our moments and meetings
can be sacramental, if we live in
awareness of whose we are._

—LAVON BAYLER

Saturday, January 30

_We should be peaceful in words and
deeds and in our way of life._

—ANGELA OF FOLIGNO

Sunday, January 31

What does the Sovereign require

of you but to do justice, and to

love kindness, and to walk humbly

with your God?

—MICAH 6:8

Friendship between women can take different forms. It can run like a river, **quietly and sustainingly** through life; it can be an intermittent, sometime thing; or it can explode like a meteor, altering the atmosphere so that nothing ever feels or looks the same again.

—MOLLY HASKELL

Monday, February 1

The truth is, I had chosen to enjoy

my own company for a while.

Something I had never really done.

—WENDY NATKONG

Tuesday, February 2

When my heart speaks now,

I always listen.

—FRAN FISHER

Wednesday, February 3

Forgiveness is an essential and
primary building block for all of us
who want to live fruitful, effective,
and productive lives.

—LINDA H. HOLLIES

Thursday, February 4

What gifts can women offer as
humankind struggles to find
meaning in the present and
shape a meaningful future for
generations to come?

—LYNNE MOBBERLEY DEMING

Friday, February 5

When the mundane things that
occupy our time threaten to dull
our view of the universe,
it is time to slow down.

—MADELINE McCLENNEY-SADLER

Saturday, February 6

Teach us the freedom of risking our
individualism to join the circle of
your family and make it complete.

—SONYA H. CHUNG

Sunday, February 7

ISAIAH 58:1-9A (9B-12)

PSALM 112:1-9 (10)

1 CORINTHIANS 2:1-12 (13-16)

MATTHEW 5:13-20

Let your light so shine before others,

that they may see your good works

and give glory to [God] your Father

[and Mother] who is in heaven.

—MATTHEW 5:16

*Let us keep **sewing away at the tear** in the mantle of sisterhood so that we may turn it into something whole, something more honest, more **all-embracing,** more lasting in which we can **wrap** the cold, hungry, trembling earth and bring new life to the worried and confused people on it.*

—BÄRBEL VON WARTENBERG-POTTER

Monday, February 8

*We may have to get old, but we
don't have to stop dreaming.*

—DONNA E. SCHAPER

Tuesday, February 9

*Our greatest genius may be the
ability to prime the healing and
evolutionary circuits of one another.*

—JEAN HOUSTON

Wednesday, February 10

Mindfulness teaches us to be
fully aware of each experience,
letting nothing remain unnoticed,
taking nothing for granted.

—HOLLY W. WHITCOMB

Thursday, February 11

How easy it is to forget and
disregard the divine beauty
and light within ourselves
and in the "other."

—DEBORAH CHU-LAN LEE

Friday, February 12

Saturday, February 13

Sunday, February 14

EXODUS 24:12–18

PSALM 2 OR PSALM 99

2 PETER 1:16–21

MATTHEW 17:1–9

But Jesus came and touched them,

saying, "Rise, and have no fear."

—MATTHEW 17:7

Love does not . . . exist apart from being faithful and performing acts of hope; yet often we seem to suggest this when we make Christian love a virtue that denies the claims embodiment makes upon us—claims such as renunciation of **privilege, inclusivity,** *and* **responsibility.**

—MARCIA Y. RIGGS

Monday, February 15

P R E S I D E N T S '   D A Y

You can't teach a person anything.
You can create an environment in
which the person can look within,
unlocking the treasures of the past
and discovering the wisdom there.

—TRISH HERBERT

Tuesday, February 16

Just as we are sustained physically
by the food we eat, we are also
sustained spiritually, moment by
moment, as often as we eat,
as often as we drink.

—JEAN M. BLOMQUIST

Wednesday, February 17

Let the chaff of my irritation at not

having all the answers burn to ash.

—KATHLEEN CROCKFORD ACKLEY

Thursday, February 18

We stumble into prayer again and

whisper soft the dearest, fearest of

our thoughts. Lent comes.

—MAREN C. TIRABASSI

Friday, February 19

_____
_____
_____
_____
_____
_____
_____
_____
_____

The journey of ever-greater
spiritual awareness is not to be
undertaken lightly.
—MARGARET GUENTHER

Saturday, February 20

_____
_____
_____
_____
_____
_____
_____
_____
_____

What is essential for taking back
a yesterday is understanding
that you are not alone, even
in the wilderness.
—LINDA H. HOLLIES

Sunday, February 21

GENESIS 2:15–17; 3:1–7

PSALM 32

ROMANS 5:12–19

MATTHEW 4:1–11

You shall worship the Sovereign
your God, and God only
shall you serve.

—MATTHEW 4:10B

*I am here alone for the first time in weeks, to take up my "real" life again at last. That is what is strange—that friends, even passionate love, are not my real life unless there is **time alone** in which to explore and to discover what is happening or has happened. Without the interruptions, nourishing and maddening, this life would become arid. Yet I taste it fully only when I am alone here and* **"the house and I resume old conversations."**

—MAY SARTON

Monday, February 22

_An image is motionless,
timeless. . . . But language
moves . . . in history,
the past melting and rushing
toward the future._

—ALICIA OSTRIKER

Tuesday, February 23

_Many have found in our women
friends a source of inexhaustible
patience, supportiveness and
discernment, that mirrors what we
often seek in prayer._

—JANET MORLEY

Wednesday, February 24

*The season of Lent is a time
to reflect on the cross and its
meaning for our lives.*

—MYRA B. NAGEL

Thursday, February 25

*I believe we each choose our
journey and discover what life
is about in our own way.*

—JODY MILLER STEVENSON

Friday, February 26

Gifts of the heart are what
memories are made of.
—SHERYL NICHOLSON

Saturday, February 27

When we are involved in an
embodiment experience, we are often
in such a state of intense creative
concentration . . . that we lose track
of time and the needs of our egos.
—HOLLY W. WHITCOMB

Sunday, February 28

GENESIS 12:1-4A

PSALM 121

ROMANS 4:1-5, 13-17

JOHN 3:1-17 OR MATTHEW 17:1-9

That which is born of the flesh
is flesh, and that which is born
of the Spirit is spirit.

—JOHN 3:6

*I am a woman giving **birth to myself** feeling excited, tired, expectant, trusting in my own **goodness,** healing old **wounds,** discovering new **muscles,** and unwilling, day by day, to tie myself to the stake of oppression.*

—THE MUD FLOWER COLLECTIVE

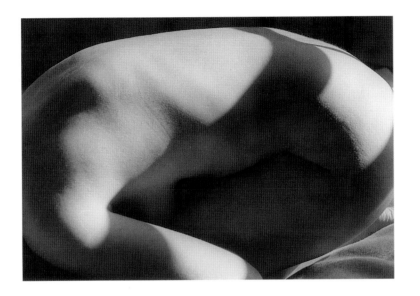

Monday, March 1

We are of the world and of each
other, and the power that is in us
is a great, if not invincible, power.

—STARHAWK

Tuesday, March 2

If women's stories are not told,
the depth of women's souls
will not be known.

—CAROL P. CHRIST

Wednesday, March 3

We offer ourselves as God's grace
one to the other.

—NELLE MORTON

Thursday, March 4

Move ahead in faith, praising God
for the new life that is yours.

—LAVON BAYLER

Friday, March 5

It is through prayer . . . that one will be given the most powerful light to see God and self.

—ANGELA OF FOLIGNO

Saturday, March 6

We live most of our life oblivious to our true identity as persons created and provided for by God.

—WENDY MILLER

Sunday, March 7

EXODUS 17:1–7

PSALM 95

ROMANS 5:1–11

JOHN 4:5–42

For this is our God, and we are

the people of God's pasture,

and the sheep of God's hand.

—PSALM 95:7

*Prayer not only provides solace in our pain, but quiets our spirits so we may move past **surface** answers and self-deception to **hear** the heart of our **deepest** desire, the heart of God within us.*

—JEAN M. BLOMQUIST

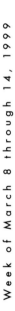

Monday, March 8

INTERNATIONAL WOMEN'S DAY

*By unlocking the past, we
open ourselves to a deeper
understanding of who we are
in the present and, therefore, who
we might become in the future.*

—BATYA PODOS

Tuesday, March 9

*Sometimes we do not know
what we think until we write it.
Writing unlocks meaning.*

—ELAINE M. WARD

Wednesday, March 10

In close friendships, there is a
hunger for truth, beginning with
the truth of each other.

—JANICE G. RAYMOND

Thursday, March 11

The stories we remember are
the narratives that interpret
our own lives.

—LYNDA SEXSON

Friday, March 12

*Just as a circle embraces all that is
within it, so does the Godhead
embrace all.*
—HILDEGARD OF BINGEN

Saturday, March 13

*In the past ten or fifteen years
women have begun to
trust each other.*
—ELIZABETH S. STRAHAN

Sunday, March 14

1 SAMUEL 16:1–13

PSALM 23

EPHESIANS 5:8–14

JOHN 9:1–41

God restores my soul. God leads
me in paths of righteousness for
God's name's sake.

—PSALM 23:3

*Women's **voices blaze** the theological trail in a new way, and the trail will look different when women as well as men have left their marks. . . . If we are to follow faithfully the trail God has set before us, then we must trust the Spirit to lead the **trailblazers** and to protect them when the trail leads in **new directions.***

—LOU BENDER

Monday, March 15

A God who cannot feel cannot
be alive and intimately related
to other lives.
—JOANNE CARLSON BROWN
AND REBECCA PARKER

Tuesday, March 16

In times of personal crisis,
who is there for you?
—GENEVA E. BELL

Wednesday, March 17

We are energized and empowered by
the "green-ness" of God's love.
—KATHLEEN CROCKFORD ACKLEY

Thursday, March 18

Our society's hope and our planet's
survival lie in our capacity to free
ourselves from rigid gender roles.
—RITA NAKASHIMA BROCK

Friday, March 19

In the midst of profound suffering,
God is present and new life
is possible.
—MARIE M. FORTUNE

Saturday, March 20

FIRST DAY OF SPRING

Springtime God . . . we need
your persistent love to disturb . . .
our hearts' rigidity.
—KATE COMPSTON

Sunday, March 21

EZEKIEL 37:1–14

PSALM 130

ROMANS 8:6–11

JOHN 11:1–45

Out of the depths I cry to you,

O God!

—PSALM 130:1

*Let us pray for faith . . . that supports and sustains when we must **make choices** that are complex and difficult; faith that is more than simplistic answers to life's most difficult choices.*

—MARILYN M. BREITLING

Monday, March 22

Conflict is a necessity if women are
to build for the future.

—JEAN BAKER MILLER

Tuesday, March 23

God's love goes before us in a way
we can never fully name.

—ANNE E. CARR

Wednesday, March 24

*We are freed by God's love to live
in the freshness of each new day.*

—MARY ANN NEEVEL

Thursday, March 25

*For the sake of power, it is
often necessary to set the world
upside down.*

—DEENA METZGER

Friday, March 26

Imaging creates the possible.

—JUANITA WEAVER

Saturday, March 27

Feminism created sisterhood—
a realignment of women with women.

—CONNIE ZWEIG

Sunday, March 28

MATTHEW 21:1–11/ISAIAH 50:4–9A

PSALM 118:1–2, 19–29/PSALM 31:9–16

PHILIPPIANS 2:5–11

MATTHEW 26:14–27, 66 OR MATTHEW 27:11–54

The Sovereign God has given

me the tongue of a teacher,

that I may know how to sustain

the weary with a word.

—ISAIAH 50:4

*It is no small matter to be **a witness** to another person's life story. By listening with compassion, we validate each other's lives, make suffering meaningful, and help the process of forgiving and healing to take place.*

—JEAN SHINODA BOLEN

Monday, March 29

Resurrection is finding that place
that is just for us.
—DONNA E. SCHAPER

Tuesday, March 30

All the fragmentation our
world endures is made whole
in Jesus' death.
—GENEVA M. BUTZ

Wednesday, March 31

Resurrection means that death is
overcome in those precise instances
when human beings choose life.
—JOANNE CARLSON BROWN
AND REBECCA PARKER

Thursday, April 1

MAUNDY THURSDAY

FIRST DAY OF PASSOVER

God's love is not destroyed
at Golgotha, nor diminished
by our unclear reflection of its
saving power.
—LAVON BAYLER

Friday, April 2

*Good Friday is for practicing
the art of being alive
while being certain of death.*

—DONNA E. SCHAPER

Saturday, April 3

*Who will roll away the stone for us
from the entrance to the tomb?*

—JANET ROSS-HEINER

Sunday, April 4

E A S T E R   S U N D A Y

D A Y L I G H T   S A V I N G   T I M E   B E G I N S

ACTS 10:34–43 OR JEREMIAH 31:1–6

PSALM 118:1–2, 14–24

COLOSSIANS 3:1–4 OR ACTS 10:34–43

JOHN 20:1–18 OR MATTHEW 28:1–10

Set your minds on things that are

above, not on things that are on earth.

—COLOSSIANS 3:2

Burst forth from the *cocoons* which enslave you! Fly free as the butterfly. Shine bright as the rainbow. Christ has risen! Go in peace. Go in joy.

—SUSAN RICKETTS HUFFMAN

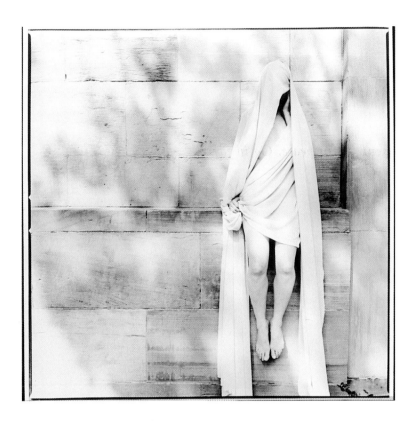

Monday, April 5

Tuesday, April 6

Wednesday, April 7

Our middle life is a progress
story, a series of little victories
over little deaths.
—GAIL SHEEHY

Thursday, April 8

Embracing honesty regarding our
physical selves allows us to pierce
the surface and reach our deeper
spiritual selves.
—MARIA HARRIS

Friday, April 9

*I decided to start anew . . .
to accept as true my own
thinking. This was one of the
best times of my life.*

—GEORGIA O'KEEFFE

Saturday, April 10

*A friend is one who remains
fundamentally a mystery,
inexhaustible, never fully known,
always surprising.*

—ANNE E. CARR

Sunday, April 11

You show me the path of life; in

your presence there is fullness of joy.

—PSALM 16:11A

Voice is central to our way of working—our channel of connection, a pathway that brings the inner psychic world of feelings and thoughts **out into the open air** of relationship where it can be **heard** by oneself and by other people.

—LYN MIKEL BROWN AND CAROL GILLIGAN

Monday, April 12

Change is the manifestation of our
ability to grow and become.
—ANNE WILSON SCHAEF

Tuesday, April 13

Practice listening to your intuition,
your inner voice.
—CLARISSA PINKOLA ESTÉS

Wednesday, April 14

Human dignity is no other than the
respect due to the image of God in us.
—MERCY ODUYOYE

Thursday, April 15

Our caregiving is important
in the universe.
—KATHY WONSON EDDY

Friday, April 16

The capacity to give one's
attention to a sufferer is a very
rare and difficult thing; it is
almost a miracle; it is a miracle.

—FRANCES YOUNG

Saturday, April 17

As a writer, it is in discovering the
particularities of my characters that
they cease to be me and begin to
grow into themselves.

—KATHERINE PATERSON

Sunday, April 18

Acts 2:14a, 36-41

Psalm 116:1-4, 12-19

1 Peter 1:17-23

Luke 24:13-35

*You have been born anew, not of
perishable seed but of imperishable,
through the living and abiding
word of God.*

—1 Peter 1:23

*Even prayer itself can become **exhausting** if we approach it as an activity willed by us and initiated by us rather than as a response to the God who has already loved us forever and who **holds us** even when we **turn away** from prayer.*

—FLORA SLOSSON WUELLNER

Monday, April 19

Week of April 19 through 25, 1999

Listening to others . . . trains us for

a more contemplative life.

—JAN JOHNSON

Tuesday, April 20

To see God face to face! All else is

vanity and vexation of the spirit.

Wisdom is in the search for God.

—KRISTIN JOHNSON INGRAM

Wednesday, April 21

Reclaiming the past to design
a new future brings with it
a certain amount of stress and
emotional response.
—VASHTI M. MCKENZIE

Thursday, April 22

E A R T H   D A Y

Many people find renewal and
strength in the presence of
Mother Earth.
—ELAINE M. WARD

Friday, April 23

---

*Whenever harm is done to
one of us, it's done to us all.*
—ALEXANDRA STODDARD

Saturday, April 24

---

*If all flowers wanted to be roses,
nature would lose her springtime beauty, and the fields
would no longer be decked out
with little wild flowers.*
—THÉRÈSE OF LISIEUX

Sunday, April 25

ACTS 2:42–47

PSALM 23

1 PETER 2:19–25

JOHN 10:1–10

God makes me lie down

in green pastures, and leads me

beside still waters.

—PSALM 23:2

*Sometimes I feel **I hear the universe** weeping or laughing, speaking to me. But I do not know. What I do know is that whether the universe has a center of consciousness or not, the sight of a **field** of flowers in the color purple or the **rainbow** must be enough to stop us from destroying all that is and wants to be.*

—CAROL P. CHRIST

Monday, April 26

The mind is just one of several
channels through which to love God.
It is the heart that burns, preserves . . .
is opened wide, decides.
—Bärbel von Wartenberg-Potter

Tuesday, April 27

I believe in holiness. I experience it
whenever I really compose,
whenever I play.
—Marge Piercy

Wednesday, April 28

Yielding seems to involve first a
fundamental attitude of receptivity . . .
a willingness to embrace what is.
—ELAINE M. PREVALLET

Thursday, April 29

Many times it seems God's word is
spoken not only through scripture
but also in the simple, ordinary
events of each day.
—ELIZABETH J. CANHAM

Friday, April 30

Healing only happens for each of us, I believe, when we embrace God in ourselves and each other.

—Katie G. Cannon

Saturday, May 1

To have a flash of intuition or insight is one thing. To begin to live by that new insight is quite another.

—Mary V. Borhek

Sunday, May 2

Acts 7:55-60

Psalm 31:1-5, 15-16

1 Peter 2:2-10

John 14:1-14

Let not your hearts be troubled;

believe in God, believe also in me.

—John 14:1

*To say I love you is to say that you are not mine, but rather your own. To love you is to advocate your rights, your space, your self, and to **struggle with you,** rather than **against you,** in our learning to claim our power in the world. . . . To love you is to be **pushed** by a power/God both terrifying and comforting, **to touch** and **be touched** by you. To love you is to sing with you, cry with you, pray with you, and act with you to re-create the world.*

—CARTER HEYWARD

Monday, May 3

*The capacity for truth-telling
requires courage.*
—THAISA FRANK AND
DOROTHY WALL

Tuesday, May 4

*All shall be well, and all manner
of things shall be well.*
—JULIAN OF NORWICH

Wednesday, May 5

Honest relationships . . . are based
on respect for the other (and one's
self) as God's own child.
—FLORA SLOSSON WUELLNER

Thursday, May 6

All through the long winter I
dream of my garden. On the first
warm day of Spring I dig my
fingers deep into the soft earth . . .
and my spirits soar.
—HELEN HAYES

Friday, May 7

It's only in the daily that we can
leave room for the extraordinary.

—JOAN D. CHITTISTER

Saturday, May 8

We must learn to listen to, hold,
and support others for their
empowerment and ours.

—RITA NAKASHIMA BROCK

Sunday, May 9

ACTS 17:22–31

PSALM 66:8–20

1 PETER 3:13–22

JOHN 14:15–21

The God who made the world and

everything in it, being Sovereign of

heaven and earth, does not live in

shrines made by human hands.

—ACTS 17:24

Visualize yourself as a **great mother** feeling all the beings upon this planet, sending forth loving thoughts of peace and harmony and certainty that the crops will be good and all will be fed. **Imagine** yourself a **great lake** sending forth endless **ripples** of compassion and care.

—DHYANI YWAHOO

Monday, May 10

When I create something, I struggle to
give it my essence, my joy, my love.
—Kathleen Crockford Ackley

Tuesday, May 11

Dwell consciously in God's presence
in the midst of all you do every day.
—Lavon Bayler

Wednesday, May 12

The Holy Spirit resurrects and
awakens everything that is.
—HILDEGARD OF BINGEN

Thursday, May 13

ASCENSION DAY

Feminism is an all-encompassing
perspective on the whole of reality.
—JANET KALVEN AND
MARY I. BUCKLEY

Friday, May 14

My impressions are scattered like
glittering stars on the dark velvet
of my memory.

—ETTY HILLESUM

Saturday, May 15

Women need to tell their stories,
and they need to be heard.

—CARROLL SAUSSY

Sunday, May 16

ACTS 1:6-14

PSALM 68:1-10, 32-35

1 PETER 4:12-14; 5:6-11

JOHN 17:1-11

*Sing to God, sing praises to God's
name; lift up a song to the one who
rides upon the clouds, whose name
is Sovereign, exult before God!*

—PSALM 68:4

*Holy Spirit, renewing energy, by you, we are born again as daughters of God; you make us **living temples** of your presence, you pray within us prayers too deep for words.*

— UNITED CHURCH OF CHRIST WOMEN

Monday, May 17

Writing is a good example
of self-abandonment.

—FLANNERY O'CONNOR

Tuesday, May 18

Prayer is honest communication:
with oneself and with God.

—KATHY KEAY

Wednesday, May 19

*As women, we need to examine
the ways in which our world can
be truly different.*
—AUDRE LORDE

Thursday, May 20

*Your love for me, O God, is like
the deepness of a well.*
—NANCY NELSON ELSENHEIMER

Friday, May 21

The diary is the only place
a woman can become real.

—ANAÏS NIN

Saturday, May 22

Christian feminism and the
spiritual vision it entails is . . .
a transforming grace for our times.

—ANNE E. CARR

Sunday, May 23

ACTS 2:1–21 OR NUMBERS 11:24–30

PSALM 104:24–34, 35B

1 CORINTHIANS 12:3B–13 OR ACTS 2:1–21

JOHN 20:19–23 OR JOHN 7:37–39

And in those days I will pour

out my Spirit on my servants,

both men and women; and they

shall prophesy.

—ACTS 2:18

I have been moved by the form of humankind.

I have **kissed** *it,*

grounding it

in faithful relationship.

—HILDEGARD OF BINGEN

Monday, May 24

*Offering sympathy and offering
to do something can be different
ways of achieving the same goal—
involvement with others.*

—DEBORAH TANNEN

Tuesday, May 25

*Associated with the feminine
element in all of us is a sense of
being-at-the-core-of-oneself.*

—ANN BELFORD ULANOV

Wednesday, May 26

*Every woman's efforts are valuable
and limited only by her own
vision and the intensity of her
belief in that vision.*

—BARBARA STARRETT

Thursday, May 27

Great delight in God overwhelms me.

—MARGARET EBNER

Friday, May 28

> I called on God, and the spirit
> of wisdom came to me. I preferred
> her to scepters and thrones,
> and I accounted wealth as nothing
> in comparison with her.
>
> —WISDOM 7:7A–8

Saturday, May 29

> Whom do I close myself against?
>
> —DEENA METZGER

Sunday, May 30

GENESIS 1:1–2:4A

PSALM 8

2 CORINTHIANS 13:11–13

MATTHEW 28:16–20

O God, our Sovereign, how majestic

is your name in all the earth!

—PSALM 8:1

*Just as hot iron put into the fire takes on the form of fire—its heat, color, power, force—and almost becomes fire itself . . . similarly, the soul, united to God and with God by the perfect fire of divine love, **gives itself,** as it were, totally and **throws itself** into God.*

—ANGELA OF FOLIGNO

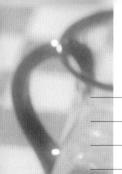

Monday, May 31

MEMORIAL DAY

*Personal memories make up
the stuff of our lives.*

—LYNDA SEXSON

Tuesday, June 1

*We need old friends to help us
grow old and new friends
to help us stay young.*

—LETTY COTTIN POGREBIN

Wednesday, June 2

We cannot afford not to fight
for growth and understanding,
even when it is painful, as it
is bound to be.

—MAY SARTON

Thursday, June 3

Praying brings us into the presence
of God who loves us.

—ELAINE M. WARD

Friday, June 4

Somehow we need to retain
what is valuable from the past
and move with courage and
vigor into the future.

—JEAN M. BLOMQUIST

Saturday, June 5

The wastelands of life around us
cannot shut out the promise
of life-giving water.

—LAVON BAYLER

Sunday, June 6

GENESIS 12:1–9/HOSEA 5:15–6:6

PSALM 33:1–12/PSALM 50:7–15

ROMANS 4:13–25

MATTHEW 9:9–13, 18–26

[Jesus] said, . . . "Go and learn
what this means, 'I desire mercy,
and not sacrifice.' For I came not to
call the righteous, but sinners."

—MATTHEW 9:13

*To work **together,** women need to be able to hear, to tell the truth, to think well about people whose concerns are different from our own, to acknowledge and tolerate conflict within and among ourselves, to face our fears and **embrace** them . . . to delight in our **differences** as revelation.*

—MARY K. WAKEMAN

Monday, June 7

To tell our stories and speak the
truth of our experience is one way
to plant a garden.
—Nancy J. Berneking and
Pamela Carter Joern

Tuesday, June 8

Our lives are given a certain
dignity by their very evanescence.
—Madeleine L'Engle

Wednesday, June 9

Time apart for play and prayer
teaches us to look at others
(and ourselves) with eyes of love.
—KATHY WONSON EDDY

Thursday, June 10

The only way we can move ahead
is by living the reality we envision.
—ADA-MARÍA ISASI-DÍAZ

Friday, June 11

*There is another sense in which
learning can be coming home.*
—MARY CATHERINE BATESON

Saturday, June 12

*Embracing age, wisdom, and
detachment leads to a sense
of ourselves as mature.*
—MARIA HARRIS

Sunday, June 18

Pray therefore to the Sovereign of

the harvest, to send out laborers

into the harvest.

—MATTHEW 9:38

*Joy does not mean an absence of frustrations or pain. Nor does it mean that I **skim easily along over the surface** of a calm life with . . . everything falling neatly and effortlessly into place.*

—MARY V. BORHEK

Monday, June 14

Freedom, after all, is like love:

the more you give to others,

the more you have.

—ALICE WALKER

Tuesday, June 15

I'm being prodded into a new

piece of soul work. . . . What would

it mean to live, welcoming all?

—SUE MONK KIDD

Week of June 14 through 20, 1999

Wednesday, June 16

*A mentor can help navigate
the often-treacherous waters of
spoken and unspoken rules and
codes of behavior.*

—VASHTI M. MCKENZIE

Thursday, June 17

*Our solitude is one of the pleasures
that only we can arrange.*

—ANNE WILSON SCHAEF

Friday, June 18

As I look back on what I have
written, I can see that the very
persons who have taken away my
time and space are those who have
given me something to say.

—KATHERINE PATERSON

Saturday, June 19

Letter writing is a peek below the
surface of our life, down where our
politics and our spirits and
our friendships are forming.

—DONNA E. SCHAPER

Sunday, June 20

GENESIS 21:8–21/JEREMIAH 20:7–13

PSALM 86:1–10, 16–17/PSALM 69:7–10 (11–15), 16–18

ROMANS 6:1B–11

MATTHEW 10:24–39

Those who find their life will lose it, and those who lose their life for my sake will find it.

—MATTHEW 10:39

*Within us and **between** us, we often discover a conflict between two basic human needs: the need to be me, to be **free,** to stake out my boundaries, and the need to be related, to be intimate, to commit myself to another.*

—CELIA ALLISON HAHN

Monday, June 21

Summer God, growing luxuriously,

blossoming with heady scents,

holding us in your warm embrace, we

need these times of perceived presence

to draw upon in cooler seasons.

—KATE COMPSTON

Tuesday, June 22

Life means movement and fun,

constant questing, making discoveries,

developing, being creative.

—FRANCES YOUNG

Week of June 21 through 27, 1999

Wednesday, June 23

Our sexuality is never ours alone;
it necessarily implies relation.
—ANNE BATHURST GILSON

Thursday, June 24

To forgive is not to forget,
but rather to re-member whatever
has been dismembered.
—CARTER HEYWARD

Friday, June 25

No wound is so trivial that the love
of God is not concerned with it.

—FLORA SLOSSON WUELLNER

Saturday, June 26

Do I repeat an experience and
deepen into it or do I go somewhere
else, indulge my curiosity,
learn another way?

—ROSELLEN BROWN

Sunday, June 27

Genesis 22:1–14/Jeremiah 28:5–9

Psalm 13/Psalm 89:1–4, 15–18

Romans 6:12–23

Matthew 10:40–42

Whoever welcomes you welcomes

me, and whoever welcomes me

welcomes the one who sent me.

—Matthew 10:40

*Often we **get stuck** in our own or our society's sense of powerlessness and we forget to get in touch with our vision for a new heaven and a new earth. We forget that we have the power to dream and to **make change** happen.*

—HOLLY W. WHITCOMB

Monday, June 28

*Difficult as it often is to grasp
someone else's pain, it is easy to
judge another's behavior.*

—MARCIA FALK

Tuesday, June 29

*As we craft our lives, there are times
of spinning and times of weaving.*

—MARGARET GUENTHER

Wednesday, June 30

*Heart-to-heart prayer transforms
our inner being and ultimately
moves us to action.*

—MYRA B. NAGEL

Thursday, July 1

CANADA DAY

Listening can be a life-giving act.

—DIANE ACKERMAN

Friday, July 2

How does human language
name God?

—GAIL RAMSHAW

Saturday, July 3

We ask God, as one would a
friend, to be present in the joy of
our shared meals and in the
suffering of the strangers.

—SALLIE MCFAGUE

Sunday, July 4

GENESIS 24:34-38, 42-49, 58-67/ZECHARIAH 9:9-12

PSALM 45:10-17 OR SONG OF SOLOMON 2:8-13/PSALM 145:8-14

ROMANS 7:15-25A

MATTHEW 11:16-19, 25-30

Take my yoke upon you, and

learn from me; for I am gentle and

lowly in heart, and you will find

rest for your souls.

—MATTHEW 11:29

*Documenting your highs and lows, your **memories** of special others and meaningful events, and especially having a record of what you have learned, what has been most important to you, is a **wonderful gift** to leave to those who **follow.** Your recorded journey may then become their pathway.*

—TRISH HERBERT

Monday, July 5

Once a woman comes to see beauty
in another woman's mind . . .
she discovers another dimension of
power that is self-fulfilling.
—NELLE MORTON

Tuesday, July 6

Dreams have the potential to
awaken us, warn us, and guide us
to wholeness and healing.
—ELAINE M. WARD

Wednesday, July 7

*Ultimately women have to tell their
own stories out of their own personal
experience and feeling, but with an
eye to the universal as well.*

—LINDA SCHIERSE LEONARD

Thursday, July 8

Sin is the failure to grow.

—KATHLEEN NORRIS

Friday, July 9

What women search for can be
as important as what we find.

—JANICE G. RAYMOND

Saturday, July 10

Any man or woman who deliberately
chooses God . . . may be sure that
he or she is loved without end.

—JULIAN OF NORWICH

Sunday, July 11

Blessed is the one whom you

choose and bring near, to dwell

in your courts!

—PSALM 65:4A

*Precisely because God is higher, deeper, and wider than any single denomination or religion can attempt to fathom, we need to widen the limited and often exclusive **image of God** that we have learned.*

—INGELINE NIELSEN

Monday, July 12

Tuesday, July 13

Wednesday, July 14

God is a cloud forming, an eagle
soaring, a voice from the wilderness
echoing through your ear.
—JUANITA HELPHREY

Thursday, July 15

God offers rivers in the deserts
of our arid lives.
—LAVON BAYLER

Friday, July 16

*We are terribly frightened of
admitting that we have been wrong
. . . yet only when we can does the
light flow in like a pardon.*

—MAY SARTON

Saturday, July 17

*The usual longevity and
flexibility of women allow most of
us to fulfill several roles.*

—NAN HUNT

Sunday, July 18

Genesis 28:10-19a/Isaiah 44:6-8

Psalm 139:1-12, 23-24/Psalm 86:11-17

Romans 8:12-25

Matthew 13:24-30, 36-43

*But if we hope for what we do not
see, we wait for it with patience.*

—Romans 8:25

Without stories a woman is lost when she comes to make the important decisions of her life. She does not learn to value her struggles, to celebrate her strengths, to comprehend her pain. *Without stories* she cannot **understand herself.**

—CAROL P. CHRIST

Monday, July 19

Writing is an audacious act
to begin with.
—THAISA FRANK AND
DOROTHY WALL

Tuesday, July 20

I think women know how to be
friends. That's what saves our lives.
—ALICE ADAMS

Wednesday, July 21

God gives us the strength and
courage to resist injustice and to
transform suffering.
—MARIE M. FORTUNE

Thursday, July 22

Come, lure our hearts with
God's desire, that we our
good once more befriend.
—J. MARY LUTI

Friday, July 23

*We are spiritual beings on a human
path rather than human beings
who may be on a spiritual path.*

—JEAN SHINODA BOLEN

Saturday, July 24

*May the Holy Spirit continue to
fan the fires of our passion for
justice and peace and inspire our
work toward that end.*

—HELEN BETENBAUGH

GENESIS 29:15–28/1 KINGS 3:5–12

PSALM 105:1–11, 45B OR PSALM 128/PSALM 119:129–136

ROMANS 8:26–39

MATTHEW 13:31–33, 44–52

The realm of heaven is like

leaven which a woman took and

hid in three measures of meal,

till it was all leavened.

—MATTHEW 13:33

*Whatever people I take into my life I take in because they challenge me and I challenge them at the deepest level. Such relationships are **rarely serene,** but they are **nourishing.***

—MAY SARTON

Monday, July 26

We look for God in the ordinary events of daily lives and listen for God in lived experiences.

—NANCY J. BERNEKING AND PAMELA CARTER JOERN

Tuesday, July 27

Weave the fabric of our lives as women in the spirit called and free.

—UNITED CHURCH OF CHRIST WOMEN

Wednesday, July 28

Give us hope and joy

sufficient for each day.

—RUTH C. DUCK

Thursday, July 29

God can be recognized in the face

of the person who lives next door.

—DOROTHEE SÖLLE

Friday, July 30

Trust is formed when intimacy is
genuine and power is shared.
—FREDRICA HARRIS THOMPSETT

Saturday, July 31

When we live most deeply in
our own hearts, we also live in the
very heart of God.
—JEAN M. BLOMQUIST

Sunday, August 1

GENESIS 32:22-31/ISAIAH 55:1-5

PSALM 17:1-7, 15/PSALM 145:8-9, 14-21

ROMANS 9:1-5

MATTHEW 14:13-21

God is gracious and merciful,

slow to anger and abounding

in steadfast love.

—PSALM 145:8

*The more deeply we let God move into our hearts then the more we experience God's **power,** the more our own **power** is released by God, and the less we wish or need to use **force** on ourselves or on anyone else. The radical change has begun within us.*

—FLORA SLOSSON WUELLNER

Monday, August 2

*Faith is ultimately a word of grace,
not judgment.*

—EMILIE M. TOWNES

Tuesday, August 3

*As men and women weigh
intimacy against responsibility,
they discover that they have
brought different weights and
measurements to the task.*

—CELIA ALLISON HAHN

Wednesday, August 4

> *Where there is no effort to create justice, there is no love.*
>
> —CARTER HEYWARD

Thursday, August 5

> *When we have friends and really share our truth with them, it changes the way things are from the inside out.*
>
> —DONNA E. SCHAPER

Friday, August 6

*Self-righteousness can be a way of
dealing with our own sense of guilt,
a way to excuse our inaction in the
face of the suffering of others.*

—MYRA B. NAGEL

Saturday, August 7

*Most people's souls are hungry
for purpose, for meaning, for
knowing that somehow they . . .
are making a difference.*

—TRISH HERBERT

Sunday, August 8

But immediately Jesus spoke to them, saying, "Take heart, it is I; have no fear."

—MATTHEW 14:27

*Do most of us have any clue as to how to be **gentle** with ourselves? When I feel physically exhausted and emotionally empty, I am trying more and more these days to stop and ask deliberately, "What do I need to help me **better care for myself** right now?"*

—HOLLY W. WHITCOMB

Monday, August 9

Many of us carry around old
baggage for years.
—DONNA E. SCHAPER

Tuesday, August 10

Writing a poem is a form of
listening, helping me discover
what's wrong . . . in my world
as well as what delights me.
—SUSAN G. WOOLDRIDGE

Wednesday, August 11

The unknown, hidden God of
mystery is a final way of speaking
of the God who is always more than
human images . . . can suggest.
—ANNE E. CARR

Thursday, August 12

Spiritual friendship demands candor,
but it is always truth spoken in love.
—MARGARET GUENTHER

Friday, August 13

Every act of gratitude is incomplete
unless it issues in a sending forth to
do works that will make for justice.

—MARIA HARRIS

Saturday, August 14

In the intensity, diversity, and rapid
pace of our daily lives, we must
remember to reconnect the holy and
sacred with the daily and ordinary.

—ELIZABETH FRANCIS CALDWELL

GENESIS 45:1–15/ISAIAH 56:1, 6–8

PSALM 133/PSALM 67

ROMANS 11:1–2A, 29–32

MATTHEW 15:(10–20), 21–28

For the gifts and call of God

are irrevocable.

—ROMANS 11:29

*Take time to notice areas of **abundance** in your life. Often scarcity, or the fear of scarcity, grabs our attention with urgency and crisis. **Abundance is quiet,** a presence that supports and **nurtures** us without demands.*

—KAY LEIGH HAGAN

Monday, August 16

Meaningful rituals provide
predictability, stability, and roots.
—MARY LoVERDE

Tuesday, August 17

What can you use to "wrap
yourself in healing" all day long?
—LINDA H. HOLLIES

Wednesday, August 18

Isn't it time that we dealt with

racism, sexism, classism, and ageism?

—CYNTHIA L. HALE

Thursday, August 19

The call to "feel with others" . . .

is a radically frightening challenge.

—DEBORAH CHU-LAN LEE

Friday, August 20

We have seen delicate flowers
emerge from rocks and the hands
of a little child bring healing to
grief and remorse.

—ANSLEY COE THROCKMORTON

Saturday, August 21

So often life offers up challenges
to our minds, our spirits,
even our very lives.

—JOAN BROWN CAMPBELL

Sunday, August 22

Do not be conformed to this world

but be transformed by the renewal

of your mind.

—ROMANS 12:2A

*When I become restless and my thoughts no longer flow to my fingertips, I take my **big yellow dog** for a long ramble through the wet woods, rebuild the fire, do chores and errands, and then pick up where I left off, to find that my unconscious has made headway in the interval.*

—MARY CATHERINE BATESON

Monday, August 23

*In the context of a culture that
encourages independence . . . the
desire to control all too easily
dictates our actions, even our prayer.*

—ELIZABETH J. CANHAM

Tuesday, August 24

*Genuine wisdom involves learning
from the wisdoms of other forgotten
or overlooked people.*

—MARIA HARRIS

Wednesday, August 25

Learn to laugh a little to yourself
and with others. Play a little to
balance your workload.

—VASHTI M. MCKENZIE

Thursday, August 26

We need to take time every day to
have gratitude and humility.

—BETTY FORD

Friday, August 27

Stopping and seeing that our lives
have become too full may well
be the beginning of a process that
can empty us and make way for
new ways of being.

—ANNE WILSON SCHAEF

Saturday, August 28

A spiritual life is never what's
happened to us. That's the easiest
thing in the world to deal with.
It's dealing with what we have
done to others that's difficult.

—NIKKI GIOVANNI

Sunday, August 29

Exodus 3:1–15/Jeremiah 15:15–21

Psalm 105:1–6, 23–26, 45c/Psalm 26:1–8

Romans 12:9–21

Matthew 16:21–28

Glory in God's holy name;

let the hearts of those who seek

God rejoice!

—Psalm 105:3

*What fun it is to cook up an **outrageous** and **flamboyant** fantasy! Making up **fantasies** and imagining outrageous acts can stretch us and allow us within a safe environment to look at acts of daring, possible consequences, and what we would really like to do if we were allowed. Fantasies can help us determine how we might incorporate a few of our **dreams** into our everyday existence.*

—HOLLY W. WHITCOMB

Monday, August 30

Week of August 30 through September 5, 1999

Flowers are my metaphor for God
reminding us that our lives are
fragile and precious.

—ALEXANDRA STODDARD

Tuesday, August 31

When the Spirit of Truth comes we
shall experience freedom, set free
from all that has closed us in.

—MERCY ODUYOYE

Wednesday, September 1

It is our center in God that gives
us the impetus and energy to reach
out and link with others.
—KATHY WONSON EDDY

Thursday, September 2

To ask questions is ultimately
to be enriched.
—FRANCES YOUNG

Friday, September 3

One of the marvelous facts of
life is that every ending carries
within itself the potential
for a new beginning.
—MARY V. BORHEK

Saturday, September 4

Justice is not about being the
power-full or the power-less,
nor is it about power-over. . . .
It is about sharing power.
—ANNE BATHURST GILSON

Sunday, September 5

EXODUS 12:1–14/EZEKIEL 33:7–11

PSALM 149/PSALM 119:33–40

ROMANS 13:8–14

MATTHEW 18:15–20

Love does no wrong to a neighbor.

—ROMANS 13:10A

*It is not mere freedom but the paradox of intimacy and distance that marks off **friendship** as a special territory in the human heart. Here as in no other human bond we stand in the tension between **freedom** and **connectedness**, in a graced space apart from cramped family quarters and the vast uncaring world.*

—CELIA ALLISON HAHN

Monday, September 6

LABOR DAY

Keep traveling, Sister! Keep traveling!
The road is far from finished.

—NELLE MORTON

Tuesday, September 7

We trust God when we are able to
let go, despite our pain and fears,
and leap into life.

—JEAN M. BLOMQUIST

Wednesday, September 8

Love is the power to act one another

into well-being, and God is love.

—JUNE C. GOUDEY

Thursday, September 9

The things of the soul must

always be considered as plentiful,

spacious, and large.

—TERESA OF AVILA

Friday, September 10

*Vulnerability is openness—to deep
engagement with the world, with
others, and with oneself.*

—CARTER HEYWARD AND
BEVERLY WILDUNG HARRISON

Saturday, September 11

ROSH HASHANAH

*God's love seeks our attentiveness,
our patience, our faithful response.*

—GENEVA M. BUTZ

Sunday, September 12

EXODUS 14:19–31/GENESIS 50:15–21

PSALM 114 OR EXODUS 15:1B–11, 20–21/PSALM 103:(1–7), 8–13

ROMANS 14:1–12

MATTHEW 18:21–35

Some people esteem one day as better than another, while others esteem all days alike. Let all be fully convinced in their own mind.

—ROMANS 14:5

*Communication is a continual **balancing** act, juggling our conflicting needs for intimacy and independence. To survive in the world, we have to act in concert with others, but to **survive as ourselves** . . . we have to act **alone**.*

—DEBORAH TANNEN

Monday, September 13

Most of us feel at least some fear
of our empowerment.
—FLORA SLOSSON WUELLNER

Tuesday, September 14

Having been gathered by love, we
are sent back to our everyday world
to share love, not as a sentimental
feeling but in caring actions.
—LAVON BAYLER

Wednesday, September 15

*If we come to terms with our
history, we free ourselves to move
toward a better future.*
—JANET KALVEN AND
MARY I. BUCKLEY

Thursday, September 16

*[The] process of woman's self-invention
makes a woman real to herself.*
—DELORES S. WILLIAMS

Friday, September 17

Women's mysteries are of the body
and the psyche.
—Jean Shinoda Bolen

Saturday, September 18

There is no hidden poet in me,
just a little piece of God that
might grow into poetry.
—Etty Hillesum

Sunday, September 19

Exodus 16:2–15/Jonah 3:10–4:11

Psalm 105:1–6, 37–45/Psalm 145:1–8

Philippians 1:21–30

Matthew 20:1–16

Seek God and God's strength,

seek God's presence continually!

—Psalm 105:4

*The shift from a deep-seated avoidance of encounter with God to a healing receptivity to God begins as we pay attention. Spiritual disciplines assist us to slow down, to hear, to pay attention, and then to listen for the word of God as it moves from our head **into our heart.***

—WENDY MILLER

Monday, September 20

YOM KIPPUR

The self-accepting person develops
a trust in her inner experience.
—CARROLL SAUSSY

Tuesday, September 21

Each of us constructs a life that
is her own central metaphor for
thinking about the world.
—MARY CATHERINE BATESON

Wednesday, September 22

*Truly, the relationship between men
and women was created to be a
relationship of mutuality.*

—LYNNE MOBBERLEY DEMING

Thursday, September 23

FIRST DAY OF FALL

*Fall is a season that creeps in
slowly, whispering change, not
wanting to scare you.*

—MARGARET A. PFEFFER

Friday, September 24

*Language reflects the way in
which we think but also informs
the way in which we think.*
—JUDITH PLASKOW AND
CAROL P. CHRIST

Saturday, September 25

*We are bound together as creatures.
We are joined together as women.*
—UNITED CHURCH
OF CHRIST WOMEN

Sunday, September 26

EXODUS 17:1–7/EZEKIEL 18:1–4, 25–32

PSALM 78:1–4, 12–16/PSALM 25:1–9

PHILIPPIANS 2:1–13

MATTHEW 21:23–32

*Do nothing from selfishness or
conceit, but in humility count
others better than yourselves.*

—PHILIPPIANS 2:3

*Since **time** is the one immaterial object which we cannot influence—neither speed up nor slow down, add to nor diminish—it is an imponderably **valuable gift**.*

—MAYA ANGELOU

Monday, September 27

*Women draw particular strength
from being part of a community.*

—BARBARA BARKSDALE CLOWSE

Tuesday, September 28

*The soul is capable of much more
than we can imagine.*

—TERESA OF AVILA

Wednesday, September 29

Women differ among themselves. We
must make room for the differences.
—ANN BELFORD ULANOV

Thursday, September 30

Silence is the best response
to mystery.
—KATHLEEN NORRIS

Friday, October 1

_By refusing to endure evil and by
seeking to transform suffering,
we are about God's work of making
justice and healing brokenness._

—MARIE M. FORTUNE

Saturday, October 2

_Take heart! Have fortitude!
Be strong!_

—KAREN ARTICHOKER

A Call for Quotes

in your reading during the past year, have you come across any quotes you would like to submit for future editions of **In Good Company?** If so, now is the time to send them in. If we use your submission, we will include your name in the acknowledgments.

When submitting quotes, please be sure that the selections are brief (1–2 sentences) and taken only from prose sources (no poetry or music). Include a photocopy of the page from which the quote is taken, along with a copy of the title page and copyright page of the book. Send your submissions to:

IN GOOD COMPANY
The Pilgrim Press
700 Prospect Avenue East
Cleveland OH 44115-1100

Sunday, October 5

Exodus 20:1–4, 7–9, 12–20/Isaiah 5:1–7

Psalm 19/Psalm 80:7–15

Philippians 3:4b–14

Matthew 21:33–46

Restore us, O God of hosts; let your

face shine that we may be saved!

—Psalm 80:7

*In prayer we open ourselves to God and share our hopes and fears, loves and hates, hungers and hurts, sorrows and joys; and the **incredible mystery** of it all is that it becomes a mutual sharing.*

—ELAINE M. WARD

Monday, October 4

New opportunities await and
abound. Never stagnate and settle.
—KATHERINE NEGERMAJIAN

Tuesday, October 5

Women tend to empower others
to feel confident to act on their
own authority.
—VASHTI M. MCKENZIE

Wednesday, October 6

Out of the left-overs of the fabric
of history, women will make a
cloth of many colours.
—MERCY ODUYOYE

Thursday, October 7

The paradox of real closeness
between two persons lies in
the ability of each to exist
independently of the other.
—MARY V. BORHEK

Friday, October 8

*There is nothing more satisfying
to one who hosts a meal than
to see guests offering one another
their full attention.*

—HOLLY W. WHITCOMB

Saturday, October 9

*We have to be willing to give up
our claim to hold on to the past.*

—LINDA H. HOLLIES

Sunday, October 10

Exodus 32:1–14/Isaiah 25:1–9

Psalm 106:1–6, 19–23/Psalm 23

Philippians 4:1–9

Matthew 22:1–14

For many are called,

but few are chosen.

—Matthew 22:14

*For years, **early morning** was a time I dreaded. In the process of waking up, my mind would run with panic. All the worries of the previous day would still be with me, **spinning around** with old regrets as well as fears for the future. I don't know how or when the change came, but now when I emerge from night, it is with **more hope than fear.***

—KATHLEEN NORRIS

Monday, October 11

*To give up our preoccupation with
evaluating others feels like death.*

—JAN JOHNSON

Tuesday, October 12

*We forget the standards God
has set for our life—that we love
God and one another—and often
think of ourselves as failures when
we are not failures at all.*

—DONNA E. SCHAPER

Week of October 11 through 17, 1999

Wednesday, October 13

Just as rising, eating, working,
and going to bed are rhythms in
our lives, nurturing our lives of
faith can also become a natural
and daily rhythm.
—ELIZABETH FRANCIS CALDWELL

Thursday, October 14

Creative use of a past heritage
cannot simply mean taking it over
with no questions asked.
—FRANCES YOUNG

Friday, October 15

*There is a spiritual basis to
attention, a humility in waiting
upon the emergence of pattern
from experience.*
—MARY CATHERINE BATESON

Saturday, October 16

*Words aren't cheap. They are
very precious.*
—KATHERINE PATERSON

Sunday, October 17

Exodus 33:12-23/Isaiah 45:1-7

Psalm 99/Psalm 96:1-9 (10-13)

1 Thessalonians 1:1-10

Matthew 22:15-22

O sing to God a new song;

sing to God, all the earth!

—Psalm 96:1

For me it's not always enough to simply experience what I **see** *in the moment. . . . It's not always enough for me to notice things, enjoy them, and take them in. . . . I want to* **bring someone** *else there also to experience a neon* **hall of mirrors** *or a luminous fog or rain.*

—SUSAN G. WOOLDRIDGE

Monday, October 18

Self-loving requires that we affirm our right to exist and our capacity to act as moral agents in the world.

—ANNE BATHURST GILSON

Tuesday, October 19

We need time and space by ourselves to appropriate the fresh sense of our worth.

—CARTER HEYWARD

Wednesday, October 20

The idea of power as effectiveness
carries the sense of simple
doing without competitiveness
or domination.

—CELIA ALLISON HAHN

Thursday, October 21

Women know that their own
experience as women has to be a
fundamental source for reflection
as they shape the future.

—ANNE E. CARR

Friday, October 22

When we look with our hearts, we
can assess our own unique gifts.

—Myra B. Nagel

Saturday, October 23

Sabbath reminds us that we are not
supposed to be in charge all the time.

—Donna E. Schaper

Sunday, October 24

DEUTERONOMY 34:1–12/LEVITICUS 19:1–2, 15–18

PSALM 90:1–6, 13–17/PSALM 1

1 THESSALONIANS 2:1–8

MATTHEW 22:34–46

And Jesus said . . . , "You shall
love the Sovereign your God with
all your heart, and with all your
soul, and with all your mind."

—MATTHEW 22:37

*Butterflies run on solar power. Cells in the design of their wings collect the warmth that **powers their flight.** When you see a butterfly at rest, perched on a flower, spreading its wings, it is said to be "basking," pausing to gather energy for future **movement.***

—KAY LEIGH HAGAN

Monday, October 25

> People with profound human needs
> and suffering do not . . . travel in a
> boat separate from mine.
>
> —SUE MONK KIDD

Tuesday, October 26

> The gratitude, wonder, and love
> we show to others are the marks
> of daily life.
>
> —ANSLEY COE THROCKMORTON

Wednesday, October 27

We work to create a more beautiful
earth . . . by coming together to the
holy tables of our lives and to the
great feast that is life itself.
—MARIA HARRIS

Thursday, October 28

Forgiveness is always required for
a life to move forward.
—LINDA H. HOLLIES

Friday, October 29

All life is a process, a pilgrimage.

—MARY V. BORHEK

Saturday, October 30

When we stop and think, we wish

that the Halloween spooks were the

worst thing we had to face.

—SUSAN RICKETTS HUFFMAN

Sunday, October 31

Joshua 3:7-17/Micah 3:5-12

Psalm 107:1-7, 33-37/Psalm 43

1 Thessalonians 2:9-13

Matthew 23:1-12

Lead a life worthy of God,

who calls you into God's own

realm and glory.

—1 Thessalonians 2:12

*As we are present to God in places of solitude away from the daily demands of work and needs of persons, gradually we notice God's presence within our **work relationships**. . . . We begin to realize that God is at work in us, and gradually our whole life embodies God's work in and through us.*

—WENDY MILLER

Monday, November 1

ALL SAINTS' DAY

When Eve bit into the apple,
she gave us the world as we know
the world—beautiful, flawed,
dangerous, full of being.
—BARBARA GRIZZUTI HARRISON

Tuesday, November 2

ELECTION DAY

Courage is crucial to putting the
past behind and moving with joy
toward an unknown future.
—BARBARA BARKSDALE CLOWSE

Wednesday, November 3

Humility, then, is being in right
relation . . . bearers of sacred spirit
with and for one another.
—CARTER HEYWARD

Thursday, November 4

We can count on God's active
presence when all other hope is gone.
—LAVON BAYLER

Friday, November 5

If truth begins in experience, then
there must be many truths.
—KAREN MCCARTHY BROWN

Saturday, November 6

Images have great power.
—ELISABETH SCHÜSSLER
FIORENZA

Sunday, November 7

Watch therefore, for you know

neither the day nor the hour.

—Matthew 25:13

*Women must learn to be patient, as their **sisters of old,** in the beautiful task of becoming midwives to the new creation they must usher into being.*

—JANET KALVEN AND MARY I. BUCKLEY

Monday, November 8

*Oh God, I thank you for having
created me as I am.*
—ETTY HILLESUM

Tuesday, November 9

*Perhaps it has always been women's
relationships with women that have
sustained their hope and vitality.*
—CARROLL SAUSSY

Wednesday, November 10

> The gift of grace we have
> received grows larger in our
> lives as we extend it to friends
> and strangers we meet.
>
> —LAVON BAYLER

Thursday, November 11

VETERANS' DAY
REMEMBRANCE DAY (CANADA)

> The road to authority is tough for
> women, and once they get there it's
> a bed of thorns.
>
> —DEBORAH TANNEN

Friday, November 12

*We serve as midwives to each
other's consciousness.*

—JEAN SHINODA BOLEN

Saturday, November 13

*Friend and friendship are categories
desperately needed on both the
divine and the human levels today.*

—ANNE E. CARR

JUDGES 4:1–7/ZEPHANIAH 1:7, 12–18

PSALM 123/PSALM 90:1–8 (9–11), 12

1 THESSALONIANS 5:1–11

MATTHEW 25:14–30

*Therefore encourage one another
and build one another up, just as
you are doing.*

—1 THESSALONIANS 5:11

Are human beings the only ones who **weep** *and* **groan,** *or can this also be predicated of the holy mystery of God who cherishes the beloved world?*

—ELIZABETH A. JOHNSON

Monday, November 15

Women's struggle and the symbolism
of the feminine have everything to
do with the mystery of being.

—ANN BELFORD ULANOV

Tuesday, November 16

Union with God is a state of peace
and harmony, joy and enhanced
power in the oneness of the All.

—ELAINE M. WARD

Wednesday, November 17

Women have much
unfinished business.
—NELLE MORTON

Thursday, November 18

Women's freedom and women's
bonding are essential for a more
human and viable world.
—JANET KALVEN AND
MARY I. BUCKLEY

Friday, November 19

Feminism . . . has brought a
rising awareness of the need for
women's power of definition,
our own language, and a means to
effect institutional change.

—CONNIE ZWEIG

Saturday, November 20

One place our private voice
goes when we are an adult is
into our journal.

—THAISA FRANK AND

DOROTHY WALL

Sunday, November 21

EZEKIEL 34:11–16, 20–24

PSALM 100/PSALM 95:1–7A

EPHESIANS 1:15–23

MATTHEW 25:31–46

Make a joyful noise to God,

all the earth.

—PSALM 100:1

*So think of the soul as a tree made for love and living only by love. . . . The circle in which this **tree's root,** the soul's love, must grow is true knowledge of herself, knowledge that is **joined to me,** who like the **circle** have neither beginning nor end.*

—CATHERINE OF SIENA

Monday, November 22

One's vocation provides a special
continuity to living.
—BARBARA BARKSDALE CLOWSE

Tuesday, November 23

God grants forgiveness along
with wisdom and strength to
face life's challenges.
—LAVON BAYLER

Week of November 22 through 28, 1999

Wednesday, November 24

The way we image the world and our place in it affects everything else.

—JANET KALVEN

Thursday, November 25

THANKSGIVING DAY

Let us give thanks for the grace-filled moments that break into our daily lives.

—LYNNE MOBBERLEY DEMING

Friday, November 26

I think of life as a mirror. If I hurt you, I've wounded myself far more than I've hurt you.

—ALEXANDRA STODDARD

Saturday, November 27

May our lives be like an autumn tree . . . branches reaching out to God, leaves falling like our years.

—BETTY SARFF

Sunday, November 28

ISAIAH 64:1–9

PSALM 80:1–7, 17–19

1 CORINTHIANS 1:3–9

MARK 13:24–37

Heaven and earth will pass away,

but my words will not pass away.

—MARK 13:31

*Thanksgiving and Advent—somehow the "thank-you" of one celebration leads into the next, and we find ourselves in the **wilderness** again, waiting for God to give us the gift of **life**.*

—GENEVA M. BUTZ

Monday, November 29

Everyone needs a safe place where
she can be healed and liberated
from her false self.
—CARROLL SAUSSY

Tuesday, November 30

During this season of waiting,
may we be open to signs of
your restoring love.
—BETH A. RICHARDSON

Wednesday, December 1

WORLD AIDS DAY

Healing is a process of finding—
if need be, creating—redemption
in suffering.

—CARTER HEYWARD

Thursday, December 2

Awakening is a recognition of one's
intense love for God.

—ELAINE M. WARD

Friday, December 3

When women and girls meet
at the crossroads of adolescence,
the intergenerational seam of
patriarchal culture opens.
—LYN MIKEL BROWN AND
CAROL GILLIGAN

Saturday, December 4

FIRST DAY OF HANUKKAH

In an age when people so seldom
find peace within themselves . . .
we light a fire called peace.
—MARY SUSAN GAST

Sunday, December 5

ISAIAH 40:1-11

PSALM 85:1-2, 8-13

2 PETER 3:8-15A

MARK 1:1-8

But according to the Sovereign's

promise we wait for new

heavens and a new earth in

which righteousness dwells.

—2 PETER 3:13

*Befriending women means continuing to befriend others even after deep friendships may be lost, or **working through** the **obstacles** in the hope that a friendship will be able to continue.*

—JANICE G. RAYMOND

Monday, December 6

_____

_____

_____

_____

_____

_____

_____

_____

_____

Thou shalt not be a superwoman—
do not try to do it all yourself.

—Vashti M. McKenzie

Tuesday, December 7

_____

_____

_____

_____

_____

_____

_____

_____

_____

_____

_____

At some deep level of the personality
. . . all change evokes the terrors of
abandonment and disillusion.

—Mary Catherine Bateson

Wednesday, December 8

What is it that draws me to prayer?

What do I find when I seek you?

—KATHLEEN CROCKFORD ACKLEY

Thursday, December 9

Solidarity is when people you

did not even know existed . . .

see you and say to you: "We

prayed for you."

—MERCY ODUYOYE

Friday, December 10

*God's creative love . . . is not merely
a superabundance of generosity, it is
also renunciation and sacrifice.*

—FRANCES YOUNG

Saturday, December 11

*Letting go is the only way
we learn to trust.*

—ELAINE M. PREVALLET

Sunday, December 12

ISAIAH 61:1–4, 8–11

PSALM 126 OR LUKE 1:47–55

1 THESSALONIANS 5:16–24

JOHN 1:6–8, 19–28

*I will greatly rejoice in the
Sovereign, my soul shall exult
in my God.*

—ISAIAH 61:10A

*This God who is ultimate, yet incarnate, whose name is love, calls everyone to unity and to the peace that is so **urgent** a task in **today's world**.*

—ANNE E. CARR

Monday, December 13

*Wisdom means listening to the
still, small voice, the whisper that
can easily be lost in the whirlwind
of busyness, expectations, and
conventions of the world.*

—JEAN M. BLOMQUIST

Tuesday, December 14

*In order to get where any of
us are today, we have all had to
shed the old and become
reconciled to the new.*

—HOLLY W. WHITCOMB

Wednesday, December 15

Moving toward other people and
moving apart are the basic steps in
life's great dance.

—CELIA ALLISON HAHN

Thursday, December 16

Our spirits hunger for
the coming of hope.

—BETH A. RICHARDSON

Friday, December 17

If work is holy, it is cooperative
rather than competitive.

—CARTER HEYWARD

Saturday, December 18

Ambiguity is the warp of life, not
something to be eliminated.

—MARY CATHERINE BATESON

Sunday, December 19

2 SAMUEL 7:1–11, 16

LUKE 1:47–55 OR PSALM 89:1–4, 19–26

ROMANS 16:25–27

LUKE 1:26–38

And the angel said to her, "Do not
be afraid, Mary, for you have found
favor with God."

—LUKE 1:30

*The rejoicing of **Mary** is the rejoicing of us all. . . . She was the sign of the readiness of humanity to **bear the seed** of the promise within its flesh.*

—WENDY M. WRIGHT

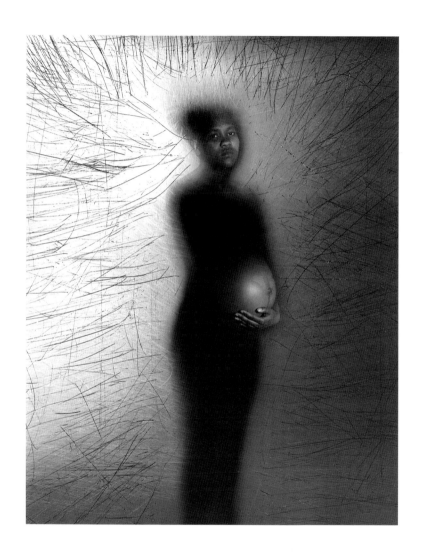

Monday, December 20

We often fail to trust our
holy wisdom because we fear
making mistakes.
—JEAN M. BLOMQUIST

Tuesday, December 21

Life is lived for itself, not for
any other benefit.
—DONNA E. SCHAPER

Wednesday, December 22

Winter God, dormant and distant

. . . we need your austerity to

nudge us into a warm compassion

for your suffering ones.

—KATE COMPSTON

Thursday, December 23

Life has confided so many

stories to me.

—ETTY HILLESUM

Friday, December 24

CHRISTMAS EVE

*Our rituals are our mangers. We and
God-with-us are birthed anew in them.*
—THE MUD FLOWER COLLECTIVE

Saturday, December 25

CHRISTMAS DAY

*Every year Christmas revives
the latent hope that . . .
defeat and despair do not have
to have the last word.*
—GENEVA M. BUTZ

Sunday, December 26

ISAIAH 61:10–62:3

PSALM 148

GALATIANS 4:4–7

LUKE 2:22–40

You shall be a crown of beauty

in the hand of the Sovereign,

and a royal diadem in the hand

of your God.

—ISAIAH 62:3

*To accept God's invitation to a creative relationship requires learning different rhythms. These **rhythms** sustain us and pull us into a **dance** set to the **heartbeat** of God.*

—JAN L. RICHARDSON

Monday, December 27

Most of us need to practice taking pride and joy in who we are and what we have experienced and achieved.

—HOLLY W. WHITCOMB

Tuesday, December 28

A friend is one whose presence is joy.

—ANNE E. CARR

Wednesday, December 29

Prayers of faith make a difference.

—LAVON BAYLER

Thursday, December 30

*We are shaped by the seasons and
delight in their changing beauty.*

—MAREN C. TIRABASSI AND

KATHY WONSON EDDY

Friday, December 31

*We must consider the effects of
our acts and decisions on those
who come after us.*

—IRENE STOCK

Saturday, January 1

*Behold, I am doing a new thing;
now it springs forth,
do you not perceive it?*

—ISAIAH 43:19A

Sunday, January 2

JEREMIAH 31:7–14 OR SIRACH 24:1–12

PSALM 147:12–20 OR WISDOM OF SOLOMON 10:15–21

EPHESIANS 1:3–14

JOHN 1:(1–9) 10–18

And the Word became flesh

and dwelt among us, full of

grace and truth.

—JOHN 1:14A

*With one **foot** planted firmly in the familiar playing field of the second half of the twentieth century, the other foot is free to dig into the new territory of the **next fifty years** beyond the millennium.*

—GAIL SHEEHY

January

S	M	T	W	T	F	S
					1	2
3	4	5	6	7	8	9
10	11	12	13	14	15	16
17	18	19	20	21	22	23
$^{24}/_{31}$	25	26	27	28	29	30

February

S	M	T	W	T	F	S
	1	2	3	4	5	6
7	8	9	10	11	12	13
14	15	16	17	18	19	20
21	22	23	24	25	26	27
28						

March

S	M	T	W	T	F	S
	1	2	3	4	5	6
7	8	9	10	11	12	13
14	15	16	17	18	19	20
21	22	23	24	25	26	27
28	29	30	31			

April

S	M	T	W	T	F	S
				1	2	3
4	5	6	7	8	9	10
11	12	13	14	15	16	17
18	19	20	21	22	23	24
25	26	27	28	29	30	

May

S	M	T	W	T	F	S
						1
2	3	4	5	6	7	8
9	10	11	12	13	14	15
16	17	18	19	20	21	22
$^{23}/_{30}$	$^{24}/_{31}$	25	26	27	28	29

June

S	M	T	W	T	F	S
		1	2	3	4	5
6	7	8	9	10	11	12
13	14	15	16	17	18	19
20	21	22	23	24	25	26
27	28	29	30			

July

S	M	T	W	T	F	S
			1	2	3
4	5	6	7	8	9	10
11	12	13	14	15	16	17
18	19	20	21	22	23	24
25	26	27	28	29	30	31

August

S	M	T	W	T	F	S
1	2	3	4	5	6	7
8	9	10	11	12	13	14
15	16	17	18	19	20	21
22	23	24	25	26	27	28
29	30	31				

September

S	M	T	W	T	F	S
			1	2	3	4
5	6	7	8	9	10	11
12	13	14	15	16	17	18
19	20	21	22	23	24	25
26	27	28	29	30		

October

S	M	T	W	T	F	S
					1	2
3	4	5	6	7	8	9
10	11	12	13	14	15	16
17	18	19	20	21	22	23
24/31	25	26	27	28	29	30

November

S	M	T	W	T	F	S
	1	2	3	4	5	6
7	8	9	10	11	12	13
14	15	16	17	18	19	20
21	22	23	24	25	26	27
28	29	30				

December

S	M	T	W	T	F	S
			1	2	3	4
5	6	7	8	9	10	11
12	13	14	15	16	17	18
19	20	21	22	23	24	25
26	27	28	29	30	31	

January

S	M	T	W	T	F	S
						1
2	3	4	5	6	7	8
9	10	11	12	13	14	15
16	17	18	19	20	21	22
$^{23}/_{30}$	$^{24}/_{31}$	25	26	27	28	29

February

S	M	T	W	T	F	S
		1	2	3	4	5
6	7	8	9	10	11	12
13	14	15	16	17	18	19
20	21	22	23	24	25	26
27	28	29				

March

S	M	T	W	T	F	S
			1	2	3	4
5	6	7	8	9	10	11
12	13	14	15	16	17	18
19	20	21	22	23	24	25
26	27	28	29	30	31	

April

S	M	T	W	T	F	S
						1
2	3	4	5	6	7	8
9	10	11	12	13	14	15
16	17	18	19	20	21	22
$^{23}/_{30}$	24	25	26	27	28	29

May

S	M	T	W	T	F	S
	1	2	3	4	5	6
7	8	9	10	11	12	13
14	15	16	17	18	19	20
21	22	23	24	25	26	27
28	29	30	31			

June

S	M	T	W	T	F	S
				1	2	3
4	5	6	7	8	9	10
11	12	13	14	15	16	17
18	19	20	21	22	23	24
25	26	27	28	29	30	

July

S	M	T	W	T	F	S
						1
2	3	4	5	6	7	8
9	10	11	12	13	14	15
16	17	18	19	20	21	22
$^{23}/_{30}$	$^{24}/_{31}$	25	26	27	28	29

August

S	M	T	W	T	F	S
		1	2	3	4	5
6	7	8	9	10	11	12
13	14	15	16	17	18	19
20	21	22	23	24	25	26
27	28	29	30	31		

September

S	M	T	W	T	F	S
					1	2
3	4	5	6	7	8	9
10	11	12	13	14	15	16
17	18	19	20	21	22	23
24	25	26	27	28	29	30

October

S	M	T	W	T	F	S
1	2	3	4	5	6	7
8	9	10	11	12	13	14
15	16	17	18	19	20	21
22	23	24	25	26	27	28
29	30	31				

November

S	M	T	W	T	F	S
			1	2	3	4
5	6	7	8	9	10	11
12	13	14	15	16	17	18
19	20	21	22	23	24	25
26	27	28	29	30		

December

S	M	T	W	T	F	S
					1	2
3	4	5	6	7	8	9
10	11	12	13	14	15	16
17	18	19	20	21	22	23
$^{24}/_{31}$	25	26	27	28	29	30

Sources

note: *Here is a list of sources from which the quotes for 1999 were taken. In compiling this list we have made every effort to find original sources for the quotes, but were unable to do so in a few cases. In addition, we are aware that a few of these sources are out of print and no longer available for purchase. The dates given in parentheses are those on which the quotes appear. All dates are for 1999 unless otherwise stated.*

Ackerman, Diane. *New York Times Magazine,* February 9, 1997. (July 1)

Ackley, Kathleen Crockford. See Kim Martin Sadler. (Feb. 17, May 10, Dec. 8)

———, ed. *In Season,* fall 1994. (March 17)

Adams, Alice. See Letty Cottin Pogrebin. (July 20)

Allenbaugh, Kay, ed. *Chocolate for a Woman's Soul.* Fireside.

Angela of Foligno. See Lynne M.

Deming, ed., *The Feminine Mystic: Readings from Early Spiritual Writers.* (Jan. 20, 30, Mar. 5, May 30)

Angelou, Maya. *Wouldn't Take Nothing for My Journey Now.* Random House. (Sept. 26)

Angle, Kimberly Greene. "Whisperings of Oak Leaves." In *Weavings: A Journal of the Christian Spiritual Life*, vol. 12, no. 3 (May/June 1997). The Upper Room. (Apr. 5)

Davies, Susan E., and Eleanor H. Haney, eds. *Redefining Sexual Ethics: A Sourcebook of Essays, Stories, and Poems.* Pilgrim Press.

Deming, Lynne Mobberley. "A New Theology of Women." See Charla H. Honea. (Feb. 4, Sept. 22)

———, ed. *The Feminine Mystic: Readings from Early Spiritual Writers.* The Pilgrim Press.

Duck, Ruth C., ed. *Flames of the Spirit: Resources for Worship.* Pilgrim Press. (July 28)

Ebner, Margaret. See Lynne M. Deming. (May 27)

Eddy, Kathy Wonson. *Writing with Light: Meditations for Caregivers in Word and Image.* United Church Press. (Apr. 15, June 9, Sept. 1)

Elsenheimer, Nancy Nelson. See Karen L. Roller. (May 20)

Estés, Clarissa Pinkola. *Women Who Run with the Wolves: Myths and Stories of the Wild Woman Archetype.* Ballantine Books. (Apr. 13)

Falk, Marcia. See Christina Büchmann and Celina Spiegel. (June 28)

Fisher, Fran. "Firewalk—Warming My 'Soul.'" See Kay Allenbaugh. (Feb. 2)

Ford, Betty. See Susan Skog. (Aug. 26)

Fortune, Marie M. "The Transformation of Suffering." See Joanne Carlson Brown and Carole R. Bohn. (Mar. 19, July 21, Oct. 1)

Frank, Thaisa, and Dorothy Wall. *Finding Your Writer's Voice: A Guide to Creative Fiction.* St. Martin's Press. (May 3, July 19, Nov. 20)

Gast, Mary Susan. See Ruth C. Duck. (Dec. 4)

Gilson, Anne Bathurst. *Eros Breaking Free: Interpreting Sexual Theo-Ethics.* Pilgrim Press. (June 23, Sept. 4, Oct. 18)

Giovanni, Nikki. See Susan Skog. (Aug. 28)

Goudey, June C. "Behold I Make All Things New." In *Prayers from the Faculty of the Seminaries of the United Church of Christ.* (Sept. 8)

Graham, George R., ed. *Jubilee: Readings through the Year from Alive Now.* Upper Room Books.

Guenther, Margaret. *Toward Holy Ground: Spiritual Directions for the Second Half of Life.* Cowley. (Feb. 4, 19, June 29, Aug. 12)

Hagan, Kay Leigh. *Prayers to the Moon: Exercises in Self-Reflection.* HarperSanFrancisco. (Aug. 15, Oct. 24)

Hahn, Celia Allison. *Sexual Paradox: Creative Tensions in Our Lives and in Our Congregations.* Pilgrim Press. (June 20, Aug. 3, Sept. 5, Oct. 20, Dec. 15)

Hale, Cynthia L. See Kim Martin Sadler. (Aug. 18)

Harris, Maria. "Foreword." See Holly W. Whitcomb. (Aug. 13, Oct. 27)

———. *Jubilee Time: Celebrating*

Tannen, Deborah. *You Just Don't Understand: Women and Men in Conversation.* Ballantine. (May 24, Sept. 12, Nov. 11)

Teresa of Avila. See Lynne M. Deming. (Sept. 9, 28)

Thérèse of Lisieux. See John Clarke. (Apr. 24)

Thompsett, Fredrica Harris. "Walking the Bounds: Historical and Theological Reflections on Ministry, Intimacy, and Power." See Katherine Hancock Ragsdale. (July 30)

Thornton, Sharon. "A Prayer of Ordination, A Prayer for All." In *Prayers from the Faculty of the Seminaries of the United Church of Christ.* (Jan. 8)

Throckmorton, Ansley Coe. See Kim Martin Sadler. (Aug. 20, Oct. 26)

Tirabassi, Maren C., and Kathy Wonson Eddy. *Gifts of Many Cultures: Worship Resources for the Global Community.* United Church Press. (Jan. 23, Feb. 18, Dec. 30)

Townes, Emilie M. "The Price of the Ticket: Racism, Sexism, Heterosexism, and the Church in the Light of the AIDS Crisis." See Susan E. Davies and Eleanor H. Haney. (Aug. 2)

Ulanov, Ann Belford. *Receiving Woman: Studies in the Psychology and Theology of the Feminine.* Westminster Press. (May 25, Sept. 29, Nov. 15)

United Church of Christ Women. See Karen L. Roller. (Jan. 15, May 16, July 27, Sept. 25)

Wakeman, Mary K. "Affirming Diversity and Biblical Tradition." See Janet Kalven and Mary I. Buckley. (June 6)

Walker, Alice. *Living by the Word: Selected Writings, 1973-1987.* Harcourt Brace Jovanovich. (June 14)

Ward, Elaine M. *Bread for the Banquet: Experiencing Life in the Spirit.* United Church Press. (Jan. 14, 22, Mar. 9, Apr. 22, June 3, July 6, Oct. 3, Nov. 16, Dec. 2)

Wartenberg-Potter, Bärbel von. *We Will Not Hang Our Harps on the Willows.* WCC Publications. (Feb. 7, Apr. 26)

Weaver, Juanita. "Images and Models—in Process." See Charlene Spretnak. (Mar. 26)

Whitcomb, Holly W. *Feasting with God: Adventures in Table Spirituality.* United Church Press. (Feb. 10, 27, June 27, Aug. 8, Aug. 29, Oct. 8, Dec. 14, Dec. 27)

Williams, Delores S. "Womanist Theology: Black Women's Voices." See Judith Plaskow and Carol P. Christ. (Jan. 18)

————. "Women as Makers of Literature." See Janet Kalven and Mary I. Buckley. (Sept. 16)

Woodman, Marion. "Conscious Femininity: Mother, Virgin, Crone." See Connie Zweig. (Feb. 13)

Wooldridge, Susan G. *Poemcrazy: Freeing Your Life with Words.* Clarkson N. Potter. (Aug. 10, Oct. 17)

Wright, Wendy M. *The Vigil: Keeping Watch in the Season of Christ's*

Coming. Upper Room Books. (Dec. 19)

Wuellner, Flora Slosson. *Prayer, Fear, and Our Powers.* Upper Room Books. (May 5, Aug. 1, Sept. 13)

————. *Prayer, Stress, and Our Inner Wounds.* The Upper Room. (Apr. 18, June 25)

Young, Frances. *Can These Dry Bones Live?: An Introduction to Christian Theology.* Pilgrim Press. (Apr. 16, June 22, Sept. 2, Oct. 14, Dec. 10)

Ywahoo, Dhyani. "Renewing the Sacred Hoop." See Judith Plaskow and Carol P. Christ. (May 9)

Zweig, Connie, ed. *To Be a Woman: The Birth of the Conscious Feminine.* Jeremy P. Tarcher. (Jan. 27, Mar. 27, Nov. 19)

About the Artists

This year's journal features the work of a talented group of artists, whose photographs were chosen with care to reflect the depth and wisdom of the quotes they accompany. We are grateful for their artistry and for their commitment to imaging women with such power and grace.

For over eighteen years photographer **John Artin Bashian** has been creating images, and since 1990 he has owned a studio in downtown Cleveland. The work used here is from his *Images of Armenia* series. Taken in 1989, six months after a devastating earthquake, these images capture the profound strength of the Armenian women.

Janine Bentivegna, a graduate of the Cooper School of Art, operates a successful commercial photography business in Cleveland Heights, Ohio. Her freelance studio and location services are utilized by national clients. Janine's work was included in *Pictures from the Edge,* a nationally touring show illuminating the issue of homelessness.

Based in a classroom of an old school building, Clevelander **Janet Century** has focused her personal work on figurative subjects. Her images continue to explore what she describes as "the human condition." Janet's extensive travels as an assignment photographer afford her the opportunity to document diverse communities throughout the United States and Europe.

Born in the Transylvanian region of Romania, and moving to the United States at age twelve, **Marius A. Chira** currently studies photography with Betsy Molnar in Cleveland. His work, which can be found in corporate and private collections, often represents itself as abstraction of figures and photographic narratives.

A native of Manhattan, **Lorraine A. DarConte** is a freelance writer and photographer living in Islip, Long Island. A former student of photographer Arthur Leipzig, Lorraine creates images that examine women and women's issues. Her figurative pieces often use satire to explore the sometimes conflicting roles of women in society.

Originally from Joliet, Illinois, **Luke Golobitsh** worked for years in national parks in Ethiopia, Colombia, and Nepal after earning a degree in wildlife biology. Since 1979 he has lived in Bonn, Germany, where his freelance photography business is based. Luke's style concentrates on the candid, spontaneous portraiture of his subjects.

Anne Hersch, a senior at Cleveland Heights High School, studies photography under the direction of Betsy Molnar. She has participated in several student and professional shows and plans to major in photography at the Rochester Institute of Technology.

Krissi Kahoun, a freelance photographer from Cleveland, recently graduated from the Colorado Institute of Art. Krissi loves to work with her hands and feels that taking the photo is just the first step. She often greatly manipulates and transforms her images during the darkroom stage.

Cleveland fine artist **Betsy Molnar** is the owner of Big Stills, a custom black-and-white photo lab serving the commercial and fine art market. Her company, in which film is processed and printed by hand, specializes in large-format work. Betsy has been recognized for her technical skills and her highly creative abstract and figurative artworks.

Originally from Bath, England, **Geoffrey Pankhurst** is currently working as a commercial photographer in Cleveland. His fine art photography, reflecting his explorations with landscapes and experimental portraits, continues to gain the attention of galleries. Geoffrey's extensive work in portraiture includes such diverse subjects as twins, Tibetans, and tattoos.

Deborah Pinter is an art therapist in Cleveland, Ohio. In a recent project she created dramatic black-and-white photographs of women posed in a classical style imitating a nineteenth-century funeral statue. Deborah sought to convey a variety of emotions in the poses, such as grief, peace, and longing.

Idris Salih, a freelance photographer living and working in New York State, focuses his work primarily on figures and portraiture of diverse subjects. His commercial fashion and personal image explorations create mood and capture personality through the use of interesting lighting and frame composition.

"My life and my vision are a single journey," says Cleveland-based artist, photographer, and arts educator **Marilyn Szalay.** "Perception and interpretation are a daily process." As a photographer, Marilyn feels thankful for all the women who have opened themselves to her camera, allowing her to express her own experience through their lives.